Smasheroo

By Hania Myers

Illustrated by Mary Hall

My name is Poppy and this is my friend Ajay.

These are Ajay's rabbits. They are soft and cuddly and like to be stroked very gently.

Sometimes Ajay's Mummy lets us sit on the grass in the sunshine and Noddy and Big Ears hop around us as we give them their favourite treats of carrot and apple.

Ajay sits in his wheelchair and his Mummy holds the rabbits up so that he can stroke them.

I really like the way their noses twitch.

This is my big brother Mikey.

He is very funny and sometimes makes us
laugh so much that our faces hurt.

Mikey can lift me up high in the air.
I like it when he turns me upside down.
Everything looks higgledy-piggledy.

Mikey is really strong. He has strong muscles.

Me and Ajay have SMA.

SMA is a short way of saying Spinal Muscular
Atrophy. Those words are so long that
I find it hard to remember them.

We were born with SMA. You can't
catch it like a cold or chicken pox.

Daddy jokes and says SMA is the beginning of the word
smasheroo. It's a funny word and makes me giggle.
It means someone who is very special and important.

Mummy and Daddy say I'm their smasheroo!

Really though, SMA means that our muscles are not
as strong as other people's, like Mikey, and they don't
work quite as well so we find some things a bit tricky.

Sometimes I fall down easily.

I can't walk quite as far or as fast as some
of my friends and I get tired quickly.

Ajay uses his electric wheelchair to help him
get about. He makes it go along himself by
using the joystick, and he can go very fast.

I have a wheelchair that I use if I have to walk
a long way. It doesn't go along by itself like
Ajay's, someone has to push it for me.

I was allowed to choose the colour I wanted.
My wheelchair is purple and has yellow
smiley faces on the wheels.

Sometimes I find it difficult to
go up and down steps.

We've got a lot of stairs in our house.
A nice man came and put some rails by my
stairs to help me get up and down them.

His drill was so loud that our whole house shook!
Rufus, our dog, ran away and hid under the table.

Ajay has got a lift to help him get up stairs.

All of his friends love having a ride
on it when they come over.

We say "Going up!" before we press the button
to start the lift and "Ding! First floor!"
when we get to the top.

Once, Ajay and his best friend Olly Small
were playing on the lift so much that
it got stuck half way up.

Ajay's Mummy was a bit cross but managed
to get it working again.

It was a really exciting day today.

It was Olly's birthday and he
had a fancy dress party.

Olly had a cowboy outfit and I wore my fairy
dress and wings. I even had a magic wand.

Millie Baxter's grandma had made her
a princess dress and a tiara with
shiny jewels.

Ajay went as a pirate. He had an eye
patch and a parrot to sit on his shoulder.

I love going to parties and
playing with my friends.

Sometimes when there are lots of
people, I get a bit frightened in case
I get knocked over and hurt.

Ajay's wheelchair helps him feel safe.
It's very heavy and it would be
difficult to knock it over.

At the party we played lots of games.

Pass the parcel was my favourite. We all sat in a circle on the floor and Olly's Daddy lifted Ajay out of his wheelchair.

William, who was dressed up as a green and yellow spotted monster, sat next to Ajay and helped him when it was his turn.

Ajay finds it a bit difficult to pass the parcel and unwrap it on his own.

I didn't win the prize but I enjoyed unwrapping one of the layers and finding a chocolate wrapped in shiny red paper hiding inside.

Some of the children were playing racing games.

Although Ajay sometimes feels a bit sad that he can't run with the other children, he was the fastest in his wheelchair and won all of his races.

I found it hard to keep up so I sat down on a bench and watched instead.

Millie came and sat next to me and let me try on her tiara.

The party was great fun.

The time flew by and it was soon time
for my Daddy to pick me up.

Olly gave me a pink balloon to take home.
Ajay's Mummy tied his balloon to his
wheelchair, it looked really good.

Millie let go of hers and the wind took it up,
up above the trees before it floated away.

She was upset and cried so Olly's
Mummy gave her another one.

All that fun at the party made me feel very tired.

When I got home I had to do my exercises.

I didn't feel like doing them but Mummy told
me that I need to do them every day to try
and keep my muscles as strong as possible.

Daddy makes my exercises fun.
He makes them into games and we make
the toys join in and do them too.

At bedtime when Daddy was tucking me into bed, I asked him why I couldn't keep up with the other children when they were racing.

My Daddy kissed me on the nose and said that everyone is good at different things.

Some people are good at running races, but others are good at painting beautiful pictures.

Some are good at writing exciting stories, others have singing voices like angels.

Just remember everyone is different and everyone is special in their own way.

Everyone is a Smasheroo!

I closed my eyes and, with a smile on my face, drifted off to sleep thinking about all the things that I might be good at.

Perhaps I'd be a great space explorer or an expert musician or even a brilliant artist.

What about a.....

The Jennifer Trust
Help for today, hope for tomorrow
For more information about Spinal Muscular Atrophy
(SMA) visit the Jennifer Trust's website **www.jtsma.org.uk**

Written by: Hania Myers Illustrations © Mary Hall 2011
Design: www.brand-mirror.com and Dickidot Ltd
Print: www.techniquestudios.com
Published by: The Jennifer Trust for Spinal Muscular Atrophy, 40 Cygnet Court,
Timothy's Bridge Road, Stratford Upon Avon, Warwickshire CV37 9NW